Working Papers II, Chapters 14-28

to accompany

Fundamental Accounting Principles

Eleventh Edition

Kermit D. Larson
The University of Texas at Austin
William W. Pyle

1987
IRWIN
Homewood, Illinois 60430

Printed in the United States of America.

ISBN 0-256-03584-9

1 2 3 4 5 6 7 8 9 VK 4 3 2 1 0 9 8 7

Contents

PROBLEM 14-1 or 14-1A

Name ________________________________

DATE		ACCOUNT TITLES AND EXPLANATION	P.R.	DEBIT	CREDIT

Income Sharing Plan	Year ________ *Calculations*		

Income Sharing Plan	Year ______ *Calculations*		

Income Sharing Plan	Year ________ *Calculations*		

CHAPTER 14 **PROBLEM 14-3 or 14-3A** **Name** ______________________

Part 1

Income Sharing Plan	Calculations				

 Name ______________________

GENERAL JOURNAL

PAGE 1

DATE		ACCOUNT TITLES AND EXPLANATION	P.R.	DEBIT	CREDIT

DATE	ACCOUNT TITLES AND EXPLANATION	P.R.	DEBIT	CREDIT

 Name ______________________

GENERAL JOURNAL

DATE		ACCOUNT TITLES AND EXPLANATION	P.R.	DEBIT	CREDIT

GENERAL JOURNAL

DATE		ACCOUNT TITLES AND EXPLANATION	P.R.	DEBIT	CREDIT

 Name ______________

GENERAL JOURNAL

DATE		ACCOUNT TITLES AND EXPLANATION	P.R.	DEBIT	CREDIT

PROBLEM 14-6 or 14-6A (Concluded)

GENERAL JOURNAL

DATE		ACCOUNT TITLES AND EXPLANATION	P.R.	DEBIT	CREDIT

 Name ______________________

Part 1

GENERAL JOURNAL

DATE		ACCOUNT TITLES AND EXPLANATION	P.R.	DEBIT	CREDIT

Part 2

DATE		ACCOUNT TITLES AND EXPLANATION	P.R.	DEBIT	CREDIT

 Name ____________

Part 1

DATE		ACCOUNT TITLES AND EXPLANATION	P.R.	DEBIT	CREDIT

Part 2

DATE		ACCOUNT TITLES AND EXPLANATION	P.R.	DEBIT	CREDIT

Part 1

Part 2

 Name ______________________

(a)

Year	Calculations	Preferred dividend per share	Common dividend per share

(b)

Year	Calculations	Preferred dividend per share	Common dividend per share

(c)

Year	Calculations	Preferred dividend per share	Common dividend per share

 Name ______________________________

1) The market value of the common stock is $______________________.

2) The par value of the preferred stock is $______________________ and the par value of the common stock is $______________________.

3) The book value of the preferred stock is $______________________ and the book value of the common stock is $______________________.

4) The book value of the preferred stock is $______________________ and the book value of the common stock is $______________________.

 Name ______________________

Part 1

GENERAL JOURNAL

DATE		ACCOUNT TITLES AND EXPLANATION	P.R.	DEBIT	CREDIT

Part 2

Part 1

GENERAL JOURNAL

DATE		ACCOUNT TITLES AND EXPLANATION	P.R.	DEBIT	CREDIT

Part 2

Date		Calculations	Book Value per share	Book Value of ______ Shares

Part 1

GENERAL JOURNAL

DATE		ACCOUNT TITLES AND EXPLANATION	P.R.	DEBIT	CREDIT

Part 2

DATE		ACCOUNT TITLES AND EXPLANATION	P.R.	DEBIT	CREDIT

CHAPTER 16 PROBLEM 16-5 Name ____________________

Part 1

DATE		ACCOUNT TITLES AND EXPLANATION	P.R.	DEBIT	CREDIT

Part 2

			ELIMINATIONS		CONSOLIDATED
			DEBIT	CREDIT	

PROBLEM 16-6 or 16-6A

Name ______________________________

	ELIMINATIONS		
	DEBIT	CREDIT	CONSOLIDATED

DATE		ACCOUNT TITLES AND EXPLANATION	P.R.	DEBIT	CREDIT

 Name ______________________

Part 1

Part 2

PERIOD ENDING	*(a)* BEGINNING-OF-PERIOD PRINCIPAL BALANCE	*(b)* PERIODIC PAYMENT	*(c)* INTEREST EXPENSE FOR THE PERIOD *(a)* × *7%*	*(d)* PORTION OF PAYMENT THAT IS PRINCIPAL *(b)* − *(c)*	*(e)* END-OF-PERIOD PRINCIPAL BALANCE *(a)* − *(d)*

Parts 3 and 4

GENERAL JOURNAL

DATE		ACCOUNT TITLES AND EXPLANATION	P.R.	DEBIT	CREDIT

Part 1

Part 2

PERIOD	BEGINNING-OF-PERIOD CARRYING AMOUNT	INTEREST EXPENSE TO BE RECORDED	INTEREST TO BE PAID THE BONDHOLDERS	DISCOUNT TO BE AMORTIZED	UNAMORTIZED DISCOUNT AT END OF PERIOD	END-OF-PERIOD CARRYING AMOUNT

Part 3

GENERAL JOURNAL

DATE		ACCOUNT TITLES AND EXPLANATION	PR	DEBIT	CREDIT

Part 1

Part 2

PERIOD	BEGINNING-OF-PERIOD CARRYING AMOUNT	INTEREST EXPENSE TO BE RECORDED	INTEREST TO BE PAID THE BONDHOLDERS	PREMIUM TO BE AMORTIZED	UNAMORTIZED PREMIUM AT END OF PERIOD	END-OF-PERIOD CARRYING AMOUNT

Part 3

GENERAL JOURNAL

DATE		ACCOUNT TITLES AND EXPLANATION	PR	DEBIT	CREDIT

GENERAL JOURNAL

DATE		ACCOUNT TITLES AND EXPLANATION	P.R.	DEBIT	CREDIT

DATE		ACCOUNT TITLES AND EXPLANATION	P.R.	DEBIT	CREDIT

 Name ____________________

GENERAL JOURNAL

DATE		ACCOUNT TITLES AND EXPLANATION	P.R.	DEBIT	CREDIT

DATE		ACCOUNT TITLES AND EXPLANATION	P.R.	DEBIT	CREDI.

Parts 1-3

GENERAL JOURNAL

DATE		ACCOUNT TITLES AND EXPLANATION	PR	DEBIT	CREDIT

Part 4

PERIOD	INTEREST-METHOD AMORTIZATION			STRAIGHT-LINE AMORTIZATION		
	BEGINNING-OF-PERIOD CARRYING AMOUNT	INTEREST EXPENSE TO BE RECORDED	INTEREST EXPENSE AS A % OF CARRYING AMOUNT	BEGINNING-OF-PERIOD CARRYING AMOUNT	INTEREST EXPENSE TO BE RECORDED	INTEREST EXPENSE AS A % OF CARRYING AMOUNT

GENERAL JOURNAL

DATE		ACCOUNT TITLES AND EXPLANATION	P.R.	DEBIT	CREDIT

		ANALYZING ENTRIES		
		DEBIT	CREDIT	

Statement of Change in Financial Position

For Year Ended December 31, 198B

Analysis of Changes in Working Capital Items

For Year Ended December 31, 198B

			Working Capital	
			INCREASES	DECREASES

 PROBLEM 18-2 or 18-2A Name ______________________________

		ANALYZING ENTRIES		
		DEBIT	CREDIT	

Statement of Change in Financial Position

For Year Ended December 31, 198B

Analysis of Changes in Working Capital Items

For Year Ended December 31, 198B

			WORKING CAPITAL	
			INCREASES	DECREASES

Statement of Change in Financial Position

For Year Ended December 31, 198B

Analysis of Changes in Working Capital Items

For Year Ended December 31, 198B

			Working Capital	
			INCREASES	DECREASES

		ANALYZING ENTRIES		
		DEBIT	CREDIT	

 Name ______________________

		ANALYZING ENTRIES		
		DEBIT	CREDIT	

Statement of Change in Financial Position

For Year Ended December 31, 198B

Analysis of Changes in Working Capital Items

For Year Ended December 31, 198B

			WORKING CAPITAL	
			INCREASES	DECREASES

		ANALYZING ENTRIES		
		DEBIT	CREDIT	

Statement of Change in Financial Position

For Year Ended December 31, 198B

Analysis of Changes in Working Capital Items

For Year Ended December 31, 198B

			WORKING CAPITAL	
			INCREASES	DECREASES

Statement of Change in Financial Position

For Year Ended December 31, 198B

PROBLEM 18-6 or 18-6A (Concluded)

		ANALYZING ENTRIES		
		DEBIT	CREDIT	

CHAPTER 19

PROBLEM 19-1 or 19-1A

Name ______________________

 Name ______________________

Part 1

Part 2

Year	*Declining-balance depreciation*	*Straight-line depre.*	*After-tax difference in methods*

Parts 3 and 4

Name ______________________

 Name ______________

Part 1

Part 2

 Name ______________________

Name ______________________________

Income Statement Trends for Years Ended December 31, 198G–8A

	198G	198F	198E	198D	198C	198B	198A
Sales							
Cost of goods sold							
Gross profit from sales							
Operating expenses							
Income before taxes							

Balance Sheet Trends, December 31, 198G–8A

	198G	198F	198E	198D	198C	198B	198A
Cash							
Accounts receivable, net							
Merchandise inventory							
Other current assets							
Long-term investments							
Plant assets, net							
Total assets							
Current liabilities							
Long-term liabilities							
Common stock							
Other contributed capital							
Retained earnings							

 Name ______________________

TRANSACTION	CURRENT RATIO	ACID-TEST RATIO	WORKING CAPITAL

Part 1

Time period	Shares outstanding adjusted for stock dividend	Portion of year	

Part 2

GENERAL JOURNAL

DATE		ACCOUNT TITLES AND EXPLANATION	P.R.	DEBIT	CREDIT

Name ______________________

GENERAL JOURNAL

DATE		ACCOUNT TITLES AND EXPLANATION	P.R.	DEBIT	CREDIT

GENERAL JOURNAL

DATE		ACCOUNT TITLES AND EXPLANATION	P.R.	DEBIT	CREDIT

 Name ____________

The Work Sheet for this problem is on page 197.

GENERAL JOURNAL

DATE		ACCOUNT TITLES AND EXPLANATION	P.R.	DEBIT	CREDIT

GENERAL JOURNAL

DATE		ACCOUNT TITLES AND EXPLANATION	P.R.	DEBIT	CREDIT

The Work Sheet for this problem is on page 198.

GENERAL JOURNAL

DATE		ACCOUNT TITLES AND EXPLANATION	P.R.	DEBIT	CREDIT

GENERAL JOURNAL

DATE		ACCOUNT TITLES AND EXPLANATION	P.R.	DEBIT	CREDIT

 Name

GENERAL JOURNAL

DATE		ACCOUNT TITLES AND EXPLANATION	P.R.	DEBIT	CREDIT

 Name

GENERAL JOURNAL

DATE		ACCOUNT TITLES AND EXPLANATION	P.R.	DEBIT	CREDIT

DATE		ACCOUNT TITLES AND EXPLANATION	P.R.	DEBIT	CREDIT

GENERAL LEDGER

Raw Materials

Factory Payroll

Goods in Process

Factory Overhead

Finished Goods

Cost of Goods Sold

JOB COST LEDGER

Job ______

Job ______

Job ______

Job ______

Job ______

JOB COST SHEET

Customer's Name *Looking Company* Job No. *10*

DATE	DIRECT MATERIALS		DIRECT LABOR		OVERHEAD COSTS APPLIED		
	REQUISITION NUMBER	AMOUNT	TIME TICKET NUMBER	AMOUNT	DATE	RATE	AMOUNT
					SUMMARY OF COSTS		
					DIR. MATERIALS ____		
					DIR. LABOR ____		
					OVERHEAD ____		
	TOTAL		TOTAL		TOTAL COST OF THE JOB ____		

JOB COST SHEET

Customer's Name *Findit Company* Job No. *12*

DATE	DIRECT MATERIALS		DIRECT LABOR		OVERHEAD COSTS APPLIED		
	REQUISITION NUMBER	AMOUNT	TIME TICKET NUMBER	AMOUNT	DATE	RATE	AMOUNT
					SUMMARY OF COSTS		
					DIR. MATERIALS ____		
					DIR. LABOR ____		
					OVERHEAD ____		
	TOTAL		TOTAL		TOTAL COST OF THE JOB ____		

RAW MATERIALS LEDGER

RAW MATERIALS LEDGER CARD

ITEM *Material A*

RECEIVED					ISSUED				BALANCE		
DATE	RECEIVING REPORT	UNITS	UNIT PRICE	TOTAL PRICE	REQUISITION	UNITS	UNIT PRICE	TOTAL PRICE	UNITS	UNIT PRICE	TOTAL PRICE
Jan. 1									*25*	*176.00*	*4,400*

RAW MATERIALS LEDGER CARD

ITEM *Material B*

RECEIVED					ISSUED				BALANCE		
DATE	RECEIVING REPORT	UNITS	UNIT PRICE	TOTAL PRICE	REQUISITION	UNITS	UNIT PRICE	TOTAL PRICE	UNITS	UNIT PRICE	TOTAL PRICE
Jan. 1									*40*	*100.00*	*4,000*

RAW MATERIALS LEDGER CARD

ITEM *Machinery Lubricant*

RECEIVED					ISSUED				BALANCE		
DATE	RECEIVING REPORT	UNITS	UNIT PRICE	TOTAL PRICE	REQUISITION	UNITS	UNIT PRICE	TOTAL PRICE	UNITS	UNIT PRICE	TOTAL PRICE
Jan. 1									*13*	*40.00*	*520*

GENERAL JOURNAL

DATE		ACCOUNT TITLES AND EXPLANATION	P.R.	DEBIT	CREDIT

DATE		ACCOUNT TITLES AND EXPLANATION	P.R.	DEBIT	CREDIT

GENERAL LEDGER

Cash

Accounts Receivable

Raw Materials

Bal. 8,920	

Goods in Process

Finished Goods

Accounts Payable

Factory Payroll

Sales

Cost of Goods Sold

Factory Overhead

FACTORY OVERHEAD LEDGER

Indirect Materials

Indirect Labor

Miscellaneous Overhead

Complete the following statements:

1. The balance of the Raw Materials account is $______ and is equal to the sum of the balances of the three accounts in the Raw Materials Ledger which are: Material A, $______; Material B, $______; and Machinery Lubricant, $______.

2. The balance of the Goods in Process account is $__________ and is equal to the sum of the direct materials, $__________ ; direct labor, $__________ ; and overhead, $__________ charged to the one unfinished job in process.

3. The balance of the Factory Overhead account is $__________ and represents (over-applied, underapplied) __________ overhead.

4. The balance of the Factory Payroll account is $__________ (debit, credit) __________ , represents __________ , and results from the recording of labor time tickets for work done after the last payroll payment.

 Name ______________________________

DATE		ACCOUNT TITLES AND EXPLANATION	P.R.	DEBIT	CREDIT

DATE		ACCOUNT TITLES AND EXPLANATION	P.R.	DEBIT	CREDIT

Name ______________________________

EXPENSE ACCOUNTS AND SERVICE DEPARTMENTS	BASES OF ALLOCATION	EXPENSE ACCT. BAL.	ALLOCATION OF EXPENSES TO DEPARTMENTS				
			OFFICE	PURCHASING			

PROBLEM 24-1 or 24-1A

Name ______________________

Parts 1 and 2

CHAPTER 24 **PROBLEM 24-2 or 24-2A** **Name** ______________________

Part 1

Part 2

Part 3

Parts 4 and 5

 Name

Parts 1 and 2

Part 3

Parts 4 and 5

CHAPTER 24 PROBLEM 24-4 or 24-4A Name ______________________

Part 1

Part 2

Part 2 (Concluded)

CHAPTER 24 **PROBLEM 24-5 or 24-5A** **Name** ______________________

Part 1

Part 2

Part 2 (Concluded)

Part 3

Part 4

PROBLEM 25-4 or 25-4A Name ______________________

Name ______________________

 Name ______

 Name ______________________

 Name ____________________

Present Value of Net Cash Flows:

Years Hence	Present Value of $1 at ___%	Net Cash Flows	Present Value of Net Cash Flows

Years Hence	Present Value of $1 at __%	Net Cash Flows	Present Value of Net Cash Flows

Years Hence	Present Value of $1 at __%	Net Cash Flows	Present Value of Net Cash Flows

 Name ______________________

Part 1

Year	Income before depr. or taxes	Depreciation	Taxes	Net Cash Flow
1				
2				
3				
4				
5				
6				

Year	Income before depr. or taxes	Depreciation	Taxes	Net Cash Flow
1				
2				
3				
4				
5				
6				

Part 2

YEARS HENCE	NET CASH FLOWS	PRESENT VALUE OF $1 AT ____%	PRESENT VALUE OF NET CASH FLOWS

PROBLEM 27-4 or 27-4A (Concluded)

Part 3

YEARS HENCE	NET CASH FLOWS	PRESENT VALUE OF $1 AT ____%	PRESENT VALUE OF NET CASH FLOWS

Part 4

 Name ______________________

 Name ____________________

Part 1

Part 2

 Name ______________________________

 PROBLEM 28-3 or 28-3A **Name** ____________________

Part 1

Part 2

Part 1

	1988	1989	1990	1991	1992	1993	TOTALS

Part 2

	1988	1989	1990	1991	1992	1993	TOTALS

Part 3

	1988	1989	1990	1991	1992	1993	TOTALS

Deferred Income Taxes
